The Savior Is Born
and Other Bible Favorites

ARCTURUS

A Message from God

Luke 1:11-12 *An angel of the Lord appeared to him, standing to the right of the altar where incense was burned. Zechariah was frightened.*

Zechariah and Elizabeth were an elderly couple who lived during the time that Herod was the king of Judea. For many years, Elizabeth had tried to have a baby, but now she was too old.

Zechariah was a priest and worked at the temple. One day while he was busy working, he looked up and saw an angel next to the altar. The angel told him his name was Gabriel and that he had come to tell Zechariah that his wife was at last going to have a baby. This baby was going to be very special. His name was to be John, and he was going to help the people who were living bad lives. They would become good again, in preparation for the coming of Jesus.

Zechariah was very surprised by this, and told the angel Gabriel that he did not believe what he had said. As punishment for his lack of faith, Gabriel told Zechariah that he would be unable to speak again until the baby was born.

Sure enough, Elizabeth became pregnant; nine months later she gave birth to a baby boy. And Zechariah was not able to speak again until that time.

People expected the baby to be named Zechariah after his father but, to everyone's surprise, Elizabeth and Zechariah insisted his name was to be John.

Did you know?

By calling their baby John, Zechariah and Elizabeth went against the tradition of naming the first son after the father.

An Angel from Heaven

Luke 1:45 "How happy you are to believe that the Lord's message to you will come true!"

When Elizabeth was about six months pregnant, God sent the angel Gabriel to Nazareth in Galilee to tell Elizabeth's young relative, Mary, that she too would give birth to a baby boy. Mary was shocked and a little afraid, for she and Joseph were not yet married.

Gabriel reassured Mary, telling her not to be afraid. He said that her baby would be the son of God and was to be called Jesus. Gabriel told Mary that the Holy Spirit would watch over her and keep her safe. He reminded Mary that her cousin Elizabeth, who was too old to have a baby, was now pregnant, and that God could make anything happen.

Mary went to Judea to visit Elizabeth. When Mary arrived, Elizabeth was filled with the Holy Spirit and her baby jumped for joy in her womb. She was moved and told Mary she was blessed. Mary couldn't understand why God had chosen her to carry His son, but Elizabeth told her God had blessed her because she had faith.

The Savior is Born

Luke 2:7 She gave birth to her first son, wrapped him in strips of cloth and laid him in a manger—there was no room for them to stay at the inn.

Did you know?

A manger is a long, narrow container into which farmers put food for their cows and horses.

Mary and Joseph were living in Nazareth in Galilee, where Joseph worked as a carpenter. One day, the Emperor Augustus decided to hold a census. He wanted a list of the names of all the people who lived in his country so he could tax them. Augustus ordered everyone to register in their own town.

Joseph's family came from Bethlehem, so he went there with Mary to register. The trip was long and difficult, especially for Mary because of the child she was carrying. So Mary rode on a donkey while Joseph walked beside her.

By the time Mary and Joseph arrived in Bethlehem, it was very busy. Joseph walked from inn to inn asking for a room, but they were all full. At last, a kind innkeeper felt sorry for the couple. He saw that Mary was heavily pregnant and told them they could sleep in his stable for the night with the animals.

Thanking the innkeeper, Joseph took Mary and the donkey to the stable. But they had hardly settled in for the night when Mary realized it was time to give birth to her baby.

When the baby Jesus was born, there was no bed to put him in, so Mary wrapped him in strips of cloth and laid him in a manger. As Jesus slept, the curious animals—sheep, cows, and goats—looked on from behind a haystack.

Not too far away, just outside Bethlehem, some shepherds were busy tending their sheep in the fields. Suddenly, an angel appeared before them in a flash of light. The angel told the shepherds not to be afraid and that he brought good news. He told them their Savior had been born and that they could go and see for themselves.

Then, as the shepherds listened, there was another flash of light and the sky was filled with a choir of angels singing songs of praise to God. When the angels left, the shepherds decided that it was time to go and see the newborn baby for themselves.

The shepherds hurried to the stable and told Mary and Joseph what the angel had said about Jesus being the Savior.

The Three Wise Men

At the time when Jesus was born, Herod was king in Judea. After Jesus' birth, some wise men were studying the stars and noticed a new star in the east. They believed that this star signaled the birth of the prophesied king, and that they should follow it and worship him.

After loading their camels, the wise men set off. But on their way to Bethlehem, the wise men lost sight of the star and stopped in Jerusalem to ask if anyone knew where they might find this new king of the Jews, because they wanted to go and worship him. When King Herod heard of this, he was furious. The Romans had made Herod king of the Jews, and he didn't want a rival king in his land! Herod sent for the priests and teachers of God's law, and asked them, "When the Savior comes, where will he be born?"

On discovering the baby would be born in Bethlehem, Herod thought of a plan. He sent for the wise men to find out when they had first seen the star.

"Go and look for the child in Bethlehem," Herod told the wise men. "When you find him, let me know, so that I can come and pray to him, too."

Believing what King Herod told them, the wise men set off in search of the child. Looking up at the night sky, they saw the star again and followed it until it stopped over the place where Jesus was sleeping.

When the wise men saw the baby Jesus in Mary's arms, they fell to their knees to worship him. Then they offered gifts to the new king—gold, frankincense, and myrrh.

That night, while the wise men slept, an angel of God came to them and told them of Herod's evil plan. The angel warned them that they should not tell him where the baby Jesus was. So, early the next day, the wise men set off for home, but instead of going back through Jerusalem, they followed the angel's advice and took a different route.

Did you know?

The Bible doesn't actually say there were three wise men, it just says "wise men." We assume there were three because they gave three gifts: gold, frankincense, and myrrh.

Herod's Order

Matthew 2:14 During the night, Joseph took the young child and his mother and escaped to Egypt.

Not long after the wise men had set off, the angel of the Lord appeared to Joseph in a dream. He told Joseph to take Mary and Jesus to Egypt, far away from Bethlehem.

"King Herod plans to harm your baby, so you must leave quickly," the angel told Joseph. "You must stay in Egypt until I appear again to tell you to return to Israel."

Meanwhile, Herod was furious when he realized the wise men had tricked him and had no intention of coming back. A cruel and evil man who had many enemies, Herod was always afraid that someone would kill him and seize his throne. So, to make sure this baby king did not grow up, he ordered his soldiers to go to Bethlehem and kill every baby boy under the age of two.

The soldiers did as Herod ordered, taking the little boys from the arms of their mothers and killing them, just because Herod was afraid of losing his kingdom.

Herod did not know that Jesus was already safe, far from Bethlehem.

The people of Bethlehem could never forget that terrible day, and they hated Herod more than ever.

Not long after this cruel event, King Herod died. As before, the angel of the Lord came to Joseph, and told him it was safe for him to take Mary and Jesus back to Bethlehem. But when they arrived in Israel, Joseph was dismayed to learn that Herod's son, Archelaus, was now the king. Instead of returning to Bethlehem, Joseph took his family back to Nazareth, where he and Mary used to live, and where he thought Jesus would not come to any harm.

As the years passed, Jesus grew up in Nazareth, and everyone who knew him loved him. This is why Jesus is sometimes called Jesus of Nazareth.

John Baptizes Jesus

> *Matthew 3:16 As soon as Jesus was baptized, he came up out of the water. Then Heaven was opened to him and he saw the Spirit of God coming down like a dove and landing on him.*

John the Baptist was very unhappy about the way people were living their lives, as they were not following God's rules. People were often unkind to each other and behaved sinfully. Deciding it was time to change things, John traveled to the banks of the River Jordan, as he knew this was a place where people gathered to tell stories and exchange news while they did their washing and collected water.

John began telling all the people who gathered at the river that they should live their lives according to God. He told them that they had to confess their sins and listen to how they could become good people.

"Soon, God will be coming to judge you all, and if you do not ask for forgiveness for your evil ways and wash yourselves in the River Jordan, you will not be allowed into Heaven," John preached.

One day while John was at the River Jordan, Jesus came from Galilee and asked John to baptize him in the river.

"Why are you coming to me for baptism?" John asked Jesus. "You are the one who should be baptizing me."

Did you know?

When people are baptized, they accept Jesus as their Savior and join the Christian Church.

John felt he was not important enough to accept this incredible honor, yet Jesus insisted.

"This is how it must be for now," he told John. "I must show that I follow God in everything I do and I must set an example for people to encourage them to confess their sins and be baptized too."

So John took Jesus into the river and poured water over his head. As Jesus' head rose up out of the water, golden rays of light suddenly shone down from the sky. A white dove soared and swooped through the air and rested upon Jesus' head. The dove was the Spirit of God, and God said to Jesus, "You are my son, the one I love, and I am very pleased with what you have done."

The Disciples are Chosen

Mark 3:14 He appointed twelve men to be with him and that he could send out to preach.

As Jesus and his disciples were at the Sea of Galilee, a huge crowd began to gather. The people had come from all over the country to see Jesus. There were so many people pushing and trying to get close to him that Jesus was afraid for his safety. He asked his disciples to fetch a boat for him. Then, climbing into the boat, Jesus finished his sermon from there.

When the crowds had left, Jesus asked his twelve most trusted disciples to follow him up a steep hill so he could speak to them privately. The disciples were the brothers James and John, Simon (whom he now called Peter) and Andrew, Philip, another James, Simon the Zealot, Thaddaeus, Bartholomew, Thomas, Matthew the tax collector, and Judas Iscariot. Judas was the disciple who eventually betrayed Jesus.

"I have chosen you to do something very important," Jesus said. "I am asking you to continue my mission to spread God's word." He told them that he had chosen them to help him teach people God's word by traveling around the towns and villages as he had done. After that, they were to travel far and wide and spread Jesus' teachings to all of God's people. In order for them to

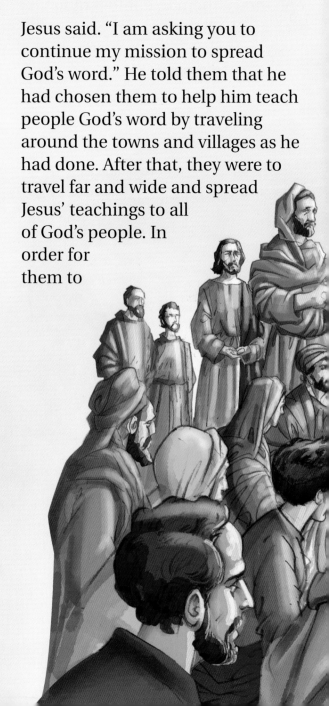

do this, Jesus gave the disciples the power to drive out evil demons from people and to heal the sick. He warned them that they would face many obstacles, but told them that God would always give them the courage they needed.

The disciples were determined to do as Jesus suggested and began to spread his teachings. From that day on, the twelve disciples came to be known as the twelve apostles.

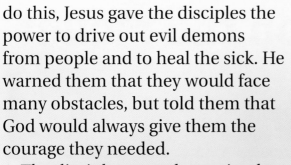

Did you know?

A disciple is someone who follows Jesus. The word is most often used when talking about the twelve main disciples, or apostles.

The Sermon on the Mount

Matthew 5:5 *"Blessed are the gentle for they shall inherit the earth."*

Everywhere Jesus went, crowds of people seemed to follow him. They had heard how he could perform miracles, so they were curious to know more about him. People wanted to be healed, or had friends and relatives they wanted Jesus to heal. But this wasn't the only reason people gathered when Jesus was nearby; they also wanted to be taught how to be good and live decent lives.

Jesus was out walking one day when a crowd gathered and asked him to speak. So he climbed up a hill and sat down. The people followed him and sat close by.

Jesus spoke first about happiness, what it was and how to find it. "You will only be truly happy when you are rewarded in Heaven for being gentle, unselfish, and pure—for trying to create a peaceful world to live in," Jesus told the crowd.

"God's creations are like salt," Jesus went on to tell the people. "But if salt loses its flavor, there is no way to make it salty again. It has become worthless—and must be thrown out."

The crowds listened in silence as Jesus continued, "You are like a light for the whole world that cannot be hidden. No one lights a lamp and puts it under a bowl; instead he puts it on the lamp-stand, where it gives light to everyone. In the same way, your

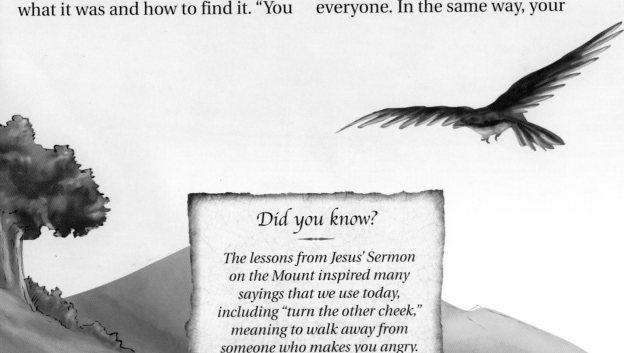

Did you know?

The lessons from Jesus' Sermon on the Mount inspired many sayings that we use today, including "turn the other cheek," meaning to walk away from someone who makes you angry.

good deeds act as a light for other people. When you lead good lives, others will see the good things you do and will praise your Father in Heaven."

Jesus went on to talk about the laws of the Ten Commandments and how they must be followed in order for people to be welcomed into Heaven. He told people that they should control their tempers and make peace with their enemies, because, when the came time for them to be judged, God would judge them for any anger they had felt toward others.

"You must love your enemies and give charitably. You must help your neighbors and friends who need it," said Jesus. "Forget about earthly riches, such as money and gold. Instead, store up riches in Heaven by doing good deeds on earth."

This sermon that Jesus taught on the hillside became known as the Sermon on the Mount.

This edition published in 2012 by Arcturus Publishing Limited
26/27 Bickels Yard, 151–153 Bermondsey Street,
London SE1 3HA
Copyright © 2012 Arcturus Publishing Limited
All rights reserved.

ISBN: 978-1-84858-674-1
CH002341US
Supplier 15, Date 0412, Print run 1753

Printed in China